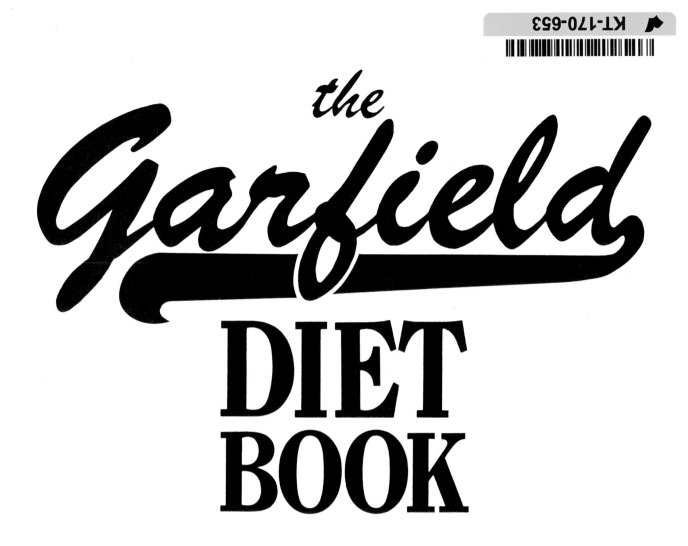

the Garfield
DIET BOOK

JIM DAVIS

RAVETTE BOOKS

First published by Ravette Books Limited 1991

Printed and bound for Ravette Books Limited,
3 Glenside Estate, Star Road,
Partridge Green, Horsham
West Sussex RH13 8RA
by PROOST, Belgium

ISBN: 1 85304 335 4